# Microworlds

## STUDENT ACTIVITY BOOK

## SCIENCE AND TECHNOLOGY FOR CHILDREN®

**NATIONAL SCIENCE RESOURCES CENTER**
Smithsonian Institution • National Academy of Sciences
Arts and Industries Building, Room 1201
Washington, DC 20560

# NSRC

The National Science Resources Center is operated by the Smithsonian Institution and the National Academy of Sciences to improve the teaching of science in the nation's schools. The NSRC collects and disseminates information about exemplary teaching resources, develops and disseminates curriculum materials, and sponsors outreach activities, specifically in the areas of leadership development and technical assistance, to help school districts develop and sustain hands-on science programs.

## STC Project Supporters

National Science Foundation
Smithsonian Institution
U.S. Department of Defense
U.S. Department of Education
John D. and Catherine T. MacArthur Foundation
The Dow Chemical Company Foundation
E. I. du Pont de Nemours & Company
Amoco Foundation, Inc.
Hewlett-Packard Company
Smithsonian Institution Educational Outreach Fund
Smithsonian Women's Committee

This project was supported, in part,
by the
**National Science Foundation**
Opinions expressed are those of the authors
and not necessarily those of the Foundation

ISBN 0-89278-950-6

Published by Carolina Biological Supply Company, 2700 York Road, Burlington, NC 27215.
Call toll free 1-800-334-5551.

This material is based upon work supported by the National Science Foundation under Grant No. ESI-9252947. Any opinions, findings, and conclusions or recommendations expressed in this material are those of the author(s) and do not necessarily reflect the views of the National Science Foundation.

CB787030109

♲ Printed on recycled paper.

# Contents

## Introduction

For a scientist, nothing is more important than
making good observations and then sharing
those observations. You will get some practice
in both these skills during this unit.

Good observations begin with using your
senses. In science class, that means your eyes,
ears, nose, and fingers.

But many things are too small to see with the
eyes alone. Some sounds or smells can't be
detected by humans.

In that case, you rely on tools. For a scientist
who wants to see very small things, the lens is
a very important tool. A lens is a curved,
transparent object that can magnify things.
Most lenses are made of glass. The microscope
is really just a set of lenses.

In this unit, you will use lenses and microscopes to view things that are too small to be seen
with your eyes alone. You will even look at tiny living objects—called microorganisms—under
your magnifying lens!

Observing is just the first step. Like a scientist, you will also record your findings. In this unit,
drawing can be an especially important way of recording what you've seen. Keep your science
notebook nearby. Date each entry and write down everything you think is important—your
predictions, your observations, and your conclusions. Share your ideas with your classmates.
See how your understanding of microworlds will grow!

| LESSON 1 | # Observing a Penny |

**Think and Wonder**

Our world is a busy place, full of sights, sounds, smells, tastes, and textures. Every day your senses are bombarded by thousands of different impressions—brightly colored flowers with their sweet perfume, horns honking, leaves crunching underfoot, or chocolate ice cream.

In this unit you will learn to take in more of your world through your sense of sight. You will become a more careful observer and learn to use tools to help you see even better.

**Materials**

*For you*

1  **Activity Sheet 1, Observing a Penny**
1  penny
1  hand lens
1  student notebook

**Find Out for Yourself**

1.  Before you begin working with magnifiers, think about what you know about them and what you want to find out.

2.  Now share what you already know about magnifiers with the class in a brief brainstorming session. Your teacher will record your ideas. Now share questions you would like to try to answer about magnifiers. Your teacher will write these down.

3.  In this lesson, you will use a hand lens to help you make very detailed observations. There are two ways to use the hand lens. See Figure 1-1.

4.  Your challenge today is to sketch both sides of a penny three different times. Your teacher will give to you **Activity Sheet 1** or show you how to set up your notebook paper to record your sketches. Now find out how observant you already are. Sketch both sides of a penny from memory.

*Figure 1-1*

*Using a hand lens*

Place the hand lens close to your eye, where a lens would be If you were wearing glasses. Hold the object in the other hand and move it back and forth slowly until it is in focus.

Or, hold the object In one place while keeping the hand lens above the object. Move the hand lens back and forth to focus.

5. Share with the class your observations of what you drew.

6. Look at the penny for 1 minute. Now cover it up. Draw what you observed. What details did you add to your drawing?

7. Next, use your hand lens to get a magnified look at your penny. Take as much time as you need. Draw what you observe. You probably will be surprised at how much more detail you will be able to add this time.

8. Turn in your pennies and your hand lenses.

9. Join in a class discussion on this topic: In science, we continually revise our ideas as we make new observations. Did that happen to you today? Tell the class how your observations changed your ideas about how a penny looks.

## Ideas to Explore

1. Clean up your penny at the polishing station using ordinary vinegar and salt. Observe your shiny penny with a hand lens. Compare it with a dirty one.

2. Do you have any other money in your pocket? Use your hand lens to observe it carefully.

3. Challenge adult family members and friends to see how much they can remember about what is on the face of a penny.

| LESSON 2 | # Communicating Your Observations |

**Think and Wonder**

Learning to make careful, detailed observations is one of the most important skills you will learn in this unit. But to be really valuable, your observations also must be recorded and communicated to others clearly, accurately, and completely.

**Materials**

*For you*

    1  student notebook

    1  hand lens

    1  **Activity Sheet 2, Communicating Your Observations**

*For your team*

    1  set of objects:

        Piece of screen wire

        Piece of burlap fabric

        Piece of yarn

      Pencil shavings

**Find Out for Yourself**

1. Briefly discuss the five senses and the kind of information each one brings to you.

2. Your teacher will quickly hide an object in the class. Then the whole class will play an observation game. Here are the rules:

   ■  The first player gives a word, a phrase, or a sentence that describes one observable property of the object your teacher has just hidden. (Example: smooth.) Remember: no naming the object and no opinions of the object.

   ■  The second player must identify the sense that brought that information to the first player. (Example: touch.)

■ Continue playing in this way until the next player cannot give an observable property of the hidden object. That player must then tell the name of the hidden object, and the game is over.

3. Now that your senses are all warmed up and ready to make observations, look at the **Activity Sheet 2** that your teacher has given to you. Or, listen while your teacher shows you how to set up a similar page in your notebook. Be sure you understand the directions before you go on.

4. Pick up the supplies you need to complete the activity. Then take the time to really observe your set of objects carefully. Record your observations both in writing and by sketching.

5. Return all the objects to a designated place.

6. Fold your **Activity Sheet** or notebook paper lengthwise so that the column marked "Name of Object" is hidden. Then exchange papers with someone from another team. Look at this new paper and try to identify the objects that your classmate has described. Jot down your answers.

7. Get back together with the person you exchanged papers with and discuss your answers. Did you both describe the same object in exactly the same way? How were your descriptions alike? How were they different?

8. Join in a whole-class discussion. Be ready to share examples of especially vivid descriptions or really accurate sketches.

## Ideas to Explore

1. Write a description for a "secret object" in the room. Make it clear and accurate. Ask the class to put their guesses into a box or envelope. How many classmates guessed correctly?

2. Create a cinquain poem featuring an object of your choice. This style of poetry will help you put some of those observable properties to good use. Below is an example of a cinquain poem.

*Figure 2-1*

*Fruit*
*Round, red*
*Hanging from trees*
*Crisp, sweet*
*Apples.*

*---Sil P.*

| LESSON 3 | # Learning about Lenses |
|---|---|

**Think and Wonder**

As you read this, you are looking through lenses in your eyes. You have a lens in each eye to focus what you see. If the lenses inside your eyes don't work well, you might need to wear a second pair of lenses outside of your eyes—eyeglasses or contact lenses. Today you will learn more about lenses, and how some can be used as magnifiers.

**Materials**

*For you*

    1  hand lens

    1  **Activity Sheet 3, Learning about Lenses**

    1  student notebook

*For your team*

    1  water-dropper bottle

    4  pieces of waxed paper (about 3-inches square)

    2  transparent acrylic spheres

    2  transparent acrylic cubes

    2  transparent acrylic cylinders

    4  pieces of newspaper (about 3-inches square)

**Find Out for Yourself**

1. Someone from your team will pick up your supplies. Teams of four will share equipment, but each of you will work individually.

2. Your teacher will give you **Activity Sheet 3** or you will be shown how to set up a page like it in your notebook. Now you can begin to learn more about lenses. First, look at your piece of newspaper, and select any small word on it of about three to five letters. Now underline the word.

**Figure 3-1**

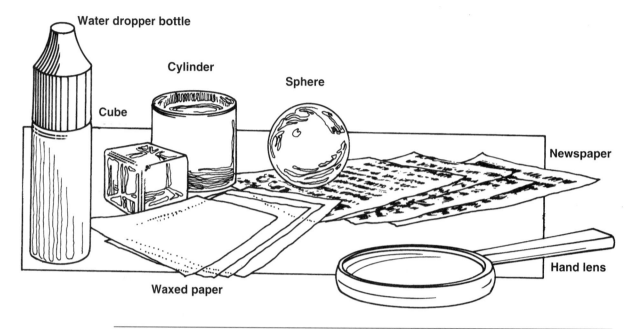

Water dropper bottle

Cylinder

Sphere

Cube

Newspaper

Hand lens

Waxed paper

3.  You will experiment with all of the acrylic shapes, but, right now, select which one you want to start with. Which you use first is not important, as long as you use them all.

4.  Now examine the shape. Predict whether it will magnify or not. Record your prediction.

5.  Test the shape. Lay it on the word you underlined on the piece of newspaper. Record the results of your test. Did the shape magnify your underlined word or not?

6.  Sketch what you see.

7.  Now do steps #4, 5, and 6 with each of the two remaining acrylic shapes.

8.  Once you have finished testing all of the solid objects to see if they magnify, it will be interesting to experiment with a liquid, water. Here is how:

    ■ Lay the piece of waxed paper on top of your underlined word. Observe. Does the waxed paper magnify your word?

    ■ Take the waxed paper off of the newspaper and use the water-dropper bottle to put *one* drop of water on the waxed paper. Examine the water drop carefully from the top and the side. Based on what you have just learned about which shapes magnify, predict whether the water drop will magnify or not. Record your prediction.

    ■ Slide the waxed paper with the water drop onto your newspaper and position the drop above your underlined word. Does the water drop magnify or not? Record in words and sketches the results of your test.

*Figure 3-2*

Waxed paper

Newspaper

9. Participate in a class discussion about which shapes acted as magnifiers and which shapes did not.

10. Look at the hand lens your teacher gives to you. How is the hand lens like the other objects that acted as magnifiers?

11. Clean up. Return all materials to the right place.

12. Listen and watch carefully as your teacher shows you the large jar of water. Will the jar of water act as a magnifier? Why or why not?

**Ideas to Explore**

1. Bring some interesting objects to class to try out with the water jar. You may also want to look at these objects in the next lesson using a hand lens.

2. Lens alert! Where are they in your everyday life? Become more aware of lenses and how important they are. Share your information with the class.

3. Do other liquids magnify? Bring in a very small quantity of a liquid you would like to test. Be sure to ask an adult's permission first.

| | |
|---|---|
| **LESSON 4** | # Looking through Lenses |

**Think and Wonder**

You have learned a lot about different lenses and which lens shapes make objects appear larger. Today you will use all these different lenses to take a close-up look at a variety of objects. As you explore, think about how you are focusing the lenses by moving them back and forth until the image is clear. Notice too, how much of an object you can see at one time. This will help you to get ready to work with a microscope in later lessons.

**Materials**

*For you*

1 **Activity Sheet 4, What Have You Learned about Lenses?**
1 marble
1 hand lens
1 student notebook

*For your team*

1 set of transparent acrylic shapes from Lesson 3
1 water-dropper bottle
4 pieces of waxed paper
1 set of objects from Lesson 2:

Screen wire

Burlap

Yarn

Pencil shavings

An assortment of objects brought in by the class

**Find Out for Yourself**

1. Take a few moments to review what you have already learned about lenses. Look at the large "magnifying jar" to help you remember.

2. Now look at a hand lens. Explain to your partner what makes it a magnifier. How is the hand lens like the large jar? Share your ideas with the class.

3. Someone from your team will pick up your supplies.

4. For about the next 20 minutes, you will be on your own, using different lenses to look at objects that interest you. Here are some guidelines to help you:

   ■ Concentrate on one object at a time. Look at the same object with different kinds of lenses. Then repeat the process for the next object.

   ■ Sketch your favorite object in your notebook. On the same page, write today's date, the name of the object, and what kind of lens you used to look through to make the drawing.

   ■ While you are working, think about what you are doing to bring the object into clear focus. How are you moving the lens?

   ■ Notice how much of an object you can see with the lens at one time. Unless the object is very small, you probably will not see all of it at once through the lens.

5. Clean up. Return everything to its proper place.

6. Discuss with your class some of the interesting observations you made.

7. Now your teacher will give you a copy of **Activity Sheet 4** and a marble. Follow the directions and work carefully to complete the sheet.

# Learning to Use the Microscope

**Who invented the microscope?**

**Who invented the microscope?**

It's hard to say. But we do know that the first person to make and use a lot of microscopes (more than 240 of them in his lifetime) was a Dutch man named Anton Leeuwenhoek.

Leeuwenhoek lived in the 1600s in the Netherlands, and he owned a store full of cloth and pincushions for sale. But the store was never open because Leeuwenhoek preferred to spend his time trying to create pieces of glass that would help him see small things.

After grinding many pieces of glass, trying to create lenses, Leeuwenhoek succeeded in making a microscope. Figure 5-1 shows what it looked like.

Most of Leeuwenhoek's microscopes were tiny things, not much larger than 1" x 2". And he had lenses to match—small, polished rock crystal, even a polished grain of sand.

Exciting things were happening all over the world at the time Leeuwenhoek lived. People from the Netherlands and other countries were exploring the seas and new worlds, trading their goods with other cultures. The painters who would become known as the "Dutch Masters" (including Rembrandt and Vermeer) were creating works of art that we instantly recognize today.

More fascinating to Leeuwenhoek than new lands or, possibly, even the new paintings, was what he could see with his simple microscopes, including one-celled plants and animals. He was the first person ever to see these creatures. One of the first times he ever saw bacteria was when he scraped some of the plaque from his teeth and looked at it under his lens. He looked at the blood of mammals and found that they have round blood cells, while other animals—birds, amphibians, and fishes—have oval ones. He was the first to see the *Volvox* (a creature you will have some experience with in a later lesson).

*Figure 5-1*

*One of
Leeuwenhoek's
microscopes
(about actual size)*

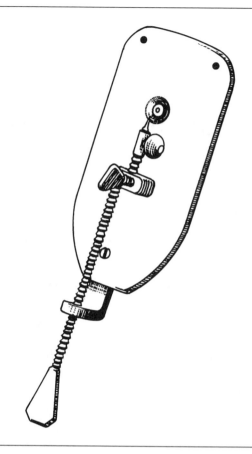

Today, only nine of Leeuwenhoek's microscopes are left. Wouldn't it be interesting to look through one? Do you think you would see different things than you see through the microscopes we have today?

## Materials

*For you*

1   microscope
1   piece of microfiche
2   slides
1   student notebook

## Find Out for Yourself

1. Read about who invented the microscope on pg. 11.

2. In order to better understand how a microscope works, join in a brief class discussion on lenses. Think about these questions:

   ■ How did you focus the hand lens?

   ■ How much of an object could you see through the lens?

   ■ Which lens shapes acted as magnifiers?

**Figure 5-2**

*Early explorers*

3. Watch while your teacher shows you the lenses in the microscope you will be using soon.

4. Pick up your supplies and take a few minutes to look at them. Compare your new microscope with the picture below. Get to know some of the names of the parts so you can follow along easily while your teacher shows you how to use the microscope correctly.

**Figure 5-3**

*Microscope*

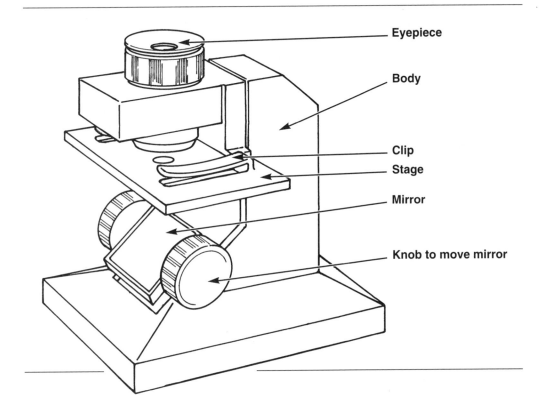

5. Watch while your teacher shows you how to place the microfiche between two slides. Then you will place the slides under the clips on the stage of the microscope. Be sure the microfiche is positioned over the hole in the stage. Careful. Handle the clips gently. They are weak and break easily.

6. Now gently twist the eyepiece to lower it as far as it will go. Your teacher will show you how.

7. Use the mirror knob to tilt the mirror so that it captures and reflects as much light as possible up onto the specimen to be examined. Warning: *Never* reflect direct sunlight up through the lenses. This can cause permanent damage to your eyes.

8. Now that you have a circle of bright light to work with, concentrate on focusing. Slowly twist the eyepiece so that it moves up and away from the stage. When you begin to see something, slow down even more and twist the eyepiece very slightly back and forth until the picture is clear.

   If you are successful, you will be able to read the message on the microfiche. If not, try again, and maybe again. This is not easy, but with practice you'll soon become skillful.

9. How much of the microfiche do you see at once? How many fleas? How many lines of print? Move your slide around a little to see other sections of the microfiche.

10. Clean up. Put away all supplies.

11. Think about what you are seeing under the microscope. How much of an object do you see?

12. Plan to bring in some printed materials to look at in Lesson 6. Especially useful would be newspapers, magazines, and comics. You might also enjoy catalogues, advertising fliers, cereal boxes, postcards, and stamps.

**Ideas to Explore**

Find out more about the fascinating world of microtechnology. Do some research on

- microchips
- medical microbots
- microwaves

**Figure 5-4**

*Microchip in the
eye of a needle*

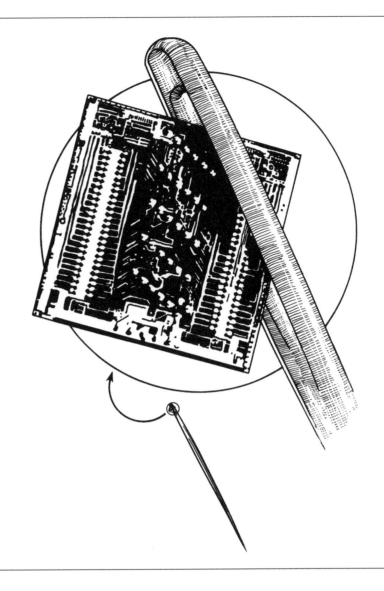

# Practicing with the Microscope

**Think and Wonder**

Things are not always what they appear to be. In this lesson you will look at some common, everyday objects with the microscope and see them in a completely new way.

**Materials**

*For you*

  1  microscope
  1  piece of screen wire
     1 or 2 pieces of tape (optional)
  1  student notebook
  1  pair of scissors (optional)
     An assortment of printed materials brought in by the class

**Find Out for Yourself**

1.  Briefly review the correct way to adjust the light and to focus the microscope.

2.  Pick up your materials.

3.  Working with the black-and-white newspaper:

    ■  Cut or rip off a slide-sized strip. This strip should show a picture with both light and dark areas.

    ■  Slip the strip under the clips and adjust the focus. What do you see?

    ■  Move the strip around so that you see lighter and darker sections of the picture. How are the lighter sections different from the darker sections?

4.  Now work with the glossy black-and-white pictures. Repeat all of the steps above in #3. What differences do you notice between the picture printed on newspaper and the picture printed on glossy paper?

5. Work with the colored pictures from newspapers next.

- Rip off or cut out a slide-sized strip of the colored paper. Try to find a picture that has at least one clear primary color (red, yellow, or blue) and one secondary color (orange. purple, or green).

- Focus first on the primary color. Describe what you see.

- Then focus on the secondary color. Describe what you see. This will be a much more complicated description.

6. Repeat all of the steps in #5 above using a colored picture from a glossy magazine. How is the glossy picture like the newspaper picture? How is it different?

7. Prepare a page in your notebook to record today's observations. Here is one way to set it up:

**Figure 6-1**

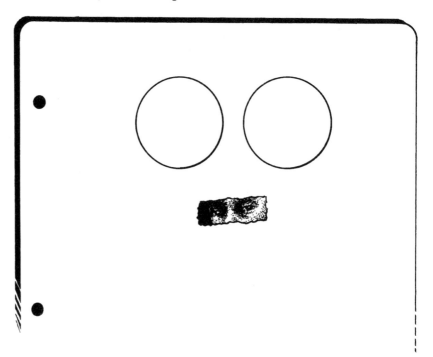

8. Select a slide-sized strip of a black-and-white newspaper picture that has a light area. Now:

- Place the piece of screen wire over the light area. If tape is available, use it to fasten the edges of screen securely to the paper.

- Slip your specimen under the clips and observe.

- Draw what you observe in one of the squares of the screen wire. How many dots are there in that one square? Count them and record the number. Be accurate.

9. Now select a slide-sized strip of a black-and-white newspaper picture that has a dark area to work with. Repeat all of the steps in #8 above using the dark area.

10. Here's a challenge for you: How small can you write? At the bottom of your notebook page, write the word "micro" as small as you possibly can. Tear off the word and look at it under the microscope.

11. Show your smallest writing sample to a partner. Whose "micro" is smaller? What kind of measuring could you do to find out?

   How could you write even smaller? What kind of tools would help?

**Ideas to Explore**

1. Find out more about a group of French artists who developed a painting technique called pointillism. They applied small dots or points of color to a surface so that they blended together when seen from a distance. You might be able to find an example of pointillism to show the class. Or, better yet, create your own work of art in the pointillist style.

*Figure 6-2*

2. Bring in some postage stamps to examine under the microscope. Notice the differences between the printed stamps (the picture is made up of dots) and the engraved stamps (the picture is made up of raised ink lines).

3. Don't forget to look at different types of paper, too. If you focus at the torn edge of the paper, you will see more of the individual fibers that make it up. Try looking at newsprint, magazines, tissue, construction paper, brown bags, cardboard, fine stationery, typing paper, and milk cartons.

# The Field of View
# (or Seeing More of Less)

**Think and Wonder**

One of the things you have been learning about a little at a time in this unit is something called the field of view. When working with water drops, for example, you were able to magnify one section of newsprint from a newspaper. What you saw through the water drop was in your field of view. The same is true of the magnifying glass and the microscope. Whatever you can see through them all at once is called your field of view. Let's get better acquainted with our microscope's field of view and learn how to measure it. You also might invent ways to measure the tiny things you see within your field of view.

**Materials**

*For you*

   1   microscope
   1   **Activity Sheet 5, Field of View**
   1   hair
   1   piece of microfiche

*For your team*

   1   set of objects from Lesson 2:
            Screen wire
            Burlap
            Yarn
            Pencil shavings
   1   water-dropper bottle
   4   pieces of newspaper
   1   pair of scissors

## Find Out for Yourself

1. Your field of view is how much of an object you can see through the microscope all at once. Get a mental picture of just one object that is about the size of a cocker spaniel and ask yourself these questions:

   ■ How much of the object could I see with just my eyes?

   ■ About how much would I see using a hand lens?

   ■ About how much would I see using a microscope?

   After you have done this mental exercise, reread the title of this lesson and explain it to a partner.

2. Watch and listen while your teacher explains more about the field of view.

3. Someone from your team will pick up your materials.

4. Now complete **Activity Sheet 5,** using your materials.

5. Clean up.

6. Join in a class discussion about field of view and measuring very small objects.

## Ideas to Explore

1. The unit used for measuring microscopic objects is called the micrometer. The symbol for micrometer is μm.

   1 micrometer (μm) = .001 mm, or one-thousandth ($1/1,000$) of a millimeter, or one-millionth ($1/1,000,000$) of a meter.

   Your hair is about 60 micrometers wide. But there are many things much smaller than that. Can you think of some? How could you use a hair as a kind of ruler to measure these tiny objects?

2. Do you have a compound microscope, one with lenses of different sizes built in, that you could share with the class?

# Preparing Slides

**Think and Wonder**

Up until now, most of the specimens that you have observed with the microscope have been relatively flat and dry. You could look at these objects either by placing them directly on the stage of the microscope or by sandwiching them between two slides for support.

When you begin to look at other kinds of things, you may find that some require more preparation. Some objects, such as a hair or a feather, may require a drop of water and two slides or a slide and a coverslip to hold them in place. These are known as wet-mount slides. (See the illustration below.)

*Figure 8-1*

*Two wet-mount slides*

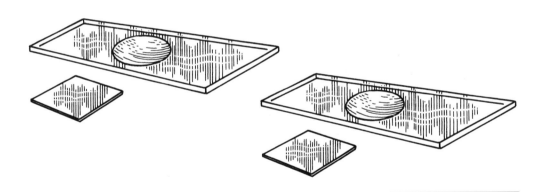

Some specimens, such as pond water or seeds, are best viewed using a well slide, also known as a depression slide. This type of slide provides a reservoir with more depth for holding thicker specimens, either wet or dry. (See the Figure 8-2.)

In this lesson you will learn how to prepare both wet-mount and well slides. You also will begin to understand the advantages of each type and when to use it.

**Figure 8-2**

*Well slide*

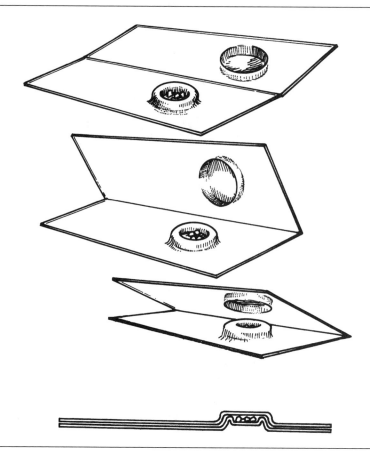

## Materials

*For you*

    1   student notebook

    1   microscope

    2   flat slides

    1   well slide

    1   coverslip

    1   hair

        Lens paper

*For your team*

    1   water-dropper bottle

    1   pair of forceps

    1   feather

    1   piece of sponge

    1   pinch of poppy seeds

    8   fish scales

## Find Out for Yourself

1. How did you make your piece of newspaper stick to the slide in the last lesson? Now you will learn other ways to prepare slides. Look at two ways that follow.

2. After your teacher has shown you the materials you will use in this lesson, someone on your team will pick up your supplies. Remember to handle the slides by the edges to avoid smudging them.

3. You may do the first two activities below in any order. Just be sure that everyone on the team gets to prepare and view all of the different types of slides.

   ***Activity 1: Preparing a wet-mount slide.*** (Use this technique for mounting the hair and the feather.)

   a. Place the specimen to be viewed in the center of a clean slide.

   b. Put a drop of water on top of the specimen.

   c. Touch one edge of the second slide or the coverslip to the drop of water, then carefully lower it on top of the specimen as illustrated below. To protect the microscope, blot any leaks before placing the slide on the stage.

---

*Figure 8-3*

*Preparing a wet-mount slide*

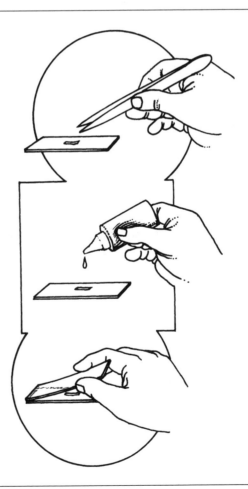

---

d. Sometimes when you make a wet-mount slide, air bubbles get trapped around the specimen. You my even mistake the bubbles for the specimen itself at first, but with a little practice you will learn to recognize them. Bubbles on a slide look like this:

**Figure 8-4**

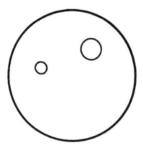

e. Make a sketch in your notebook of either the hair or the feather. Be sure to date and label it.

**Activity 2: Preparing a well slide**. (Use this technique for mounting the poppy seeds and the piece of sponge.)

a. Place the specimen to be viewed in the well. Remember, less is better. A single layer of seeds or a thin slice of sponge is easier to see.

b. Depending on the style of slide, either snap the lid shut (on the hinged style) or place a coverslip over the well.

c. Because the specimens you are viewing in the well slide have depth, only part of the specimen will be in focus at any one time. Your challenge is to learn to focus up and down over the entire surface of the object to get a complete picture of it.

d. Make a sketch in your notebook of either a poppy seed or the piece of sponge. Date and label the sketch.

**Activity 3: Experimenting with slide-making techniques**. Using the fish scales, prepare different types of slides to find out which works best for this object.

4. Clean up. You'll need to wash off your used slides at the station your teacher has provided. Gently swish them through the rinse water. Lay them on paper towels or newspaper to air dry. Polish them later with lens paper.

5. Now focus your attention on the drawings on the bulletin board. From your observations today, which specimens can you identify? A man named Robert Hooke made these drawings over 300 years ago. You will learn more about him and his amazing microscopic studies.

**Ideas to Explore**

*Figure 8-5*

1. Seeds are an interesting subject for microscope studies. If you have a spice rack at home, you may find some of the following:

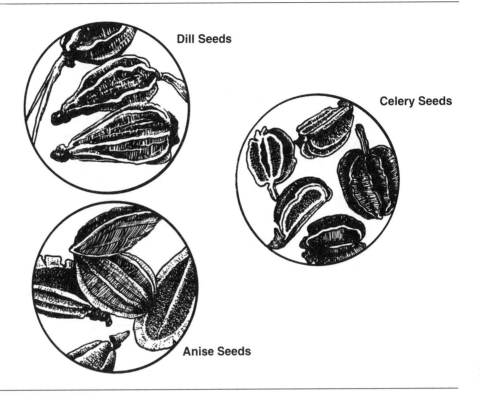

Dill Seeds

Celery Seeds

Anise Seeds

Ask permission to bring some seeds to class to look at under the microscope.

2. In Lesson 10 you will have time to observe some specimens of your own choice. Begin collecting some interesting items now.

# What Is It?

**Think and Wonder**

Let's use your new microscope skills to identify some unknown specimens. You will need to prepare your slides with great care in order to get the best possible view of these specimens. You also will need to be able to focus up and down over the entire outside surface of the specimens.

**Materials**

*For you*

    1  student notebook

    1  microscope

    1  well slide

    1  coverslip

*For your team*

    1  pinch of each of the four unknown specimens

       Transparent tape

       Lens paper

**Find Out for Yourself**

1. Join the class in a brief review of:

   ■ the different ways to prepare slides

   ■ how to focus on three-dimensional objects

   You will be using these same techniques today to observe and identify some mystery specimens.

2. Now each team needs to label their well slides from #1 to #4, one number per person. Place a small piece of tape close to the end of the slide, and write your number on it.

3. Pick up your unknown specimens together as a team, one specimen per person. Each member of the team should pick up only the specimen that has the same number as the label on his or her slide. For example, the person who has the slide labeled #1 should get only specimen #1.

4. When you return to your seat, prepare a good slide using the pinch of the specimen you picked up. Examine your slide under the microscope. If necessary, adjust the amount you put in the well so that there is only a single layer of granules. Individual granules should be clearly visible.

5. Using the information given below, identify the four unknown specimens. Work on one slide at a time. Exchange slides with a teammate until you have identified all four. Be sure to record your answers.

**Table salt**

Table salt, or sodium chloride, is easy to recognize because of its translucent, cube-shaped crystals. One of the most common minerals, it is found in great abundance both in the earth and in sea water.

*Figure 9-1A*

*Table salt*

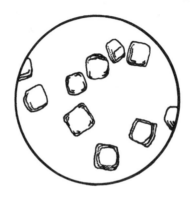

**Epsom salts**

Epsom salts, a magnesium sulfate compound, has distinctive needle-shaped crystals that range from transparent to white. This salt is named for Epsom, England, where it was prepared from the water of local mineral springs. Epsom salts is a medication used both internally as a laxative and externally to reduce inflammation.

*Figure 9-1B*

*Epsom salts*

### Quartz sand

Characteristically, quartz has a regular six-sided crystal. Quartz sand, however, shows the result of weathering. Wind, water, and temperature all contribute to breaking up quartz crystals into smaller irregular shapes of quartz sand.

**Figure 9-1C**

*Quartz sand*

### Grits

Grits is a food product made from ground corn. It is irregular in shape and ranges from opaque to translucent. Color ranges from white to pale yellow.

**Figure 9-1D**

*Grits*

6. When everyone is finished, your teacher will post the answers so that you may check your work.

7. If there is enough time, your teacher may allow you to prepare your own mystery slide with which to challenge your teammates. Carefully mix a tiny pinch of two or more of the specimens the team just identified. Make a good, clear slide. In a mixture, it is very important to be able to see individual granules. Then ask a teammate to identify what is in the mixture.

8. How could you tell one specimen from another? What differences did you see?

9. Reminder: the next lesson will focus on the objects that you bring in to observe. What are you interested in looking at? What would you like to know more about? Share your ideas with the class. Then start collecting the objects you want to look at next.

## Ideas to Explore

1. Salt crystals are easy to grow. Stir 3 tablespoons of salt into a cup of warm water. Pour the solution into a shallow pan (or put two or three droplets onto a slide) and set it on a windowsill or another warm place. As the water evaporates, salt crystals will form. Would the same thing happen with a cup of sea water?

2. Be on the lookout for other crystals around you. Share your observations with the class.

3. Here's a measurement challenge: How many hair-widths wide is each of the unknown specimens you identified (on the average)?

4. Find out more about how a microbiologist or a lab technician works. They identify "mystery slides" as part of their work every day.

# Exploring Common Objects

**Think and Wonder**

Today is your day to examine objects of special interest to you. Let your own curiosity and questions lead you to new discoveries. Good luck in your adventures in the microworld!

**Materials**

*For you*

    1   student notebook
    1   microscope
    1   well slide
    2   flat slides
    2   coverslips

*For your team*

    1   water-dropper bottle
    1   pair of forceps
    1   hand lens
    4   pieces of lens paper
        Tape

*For the class*

    An assortment of objects brought in by the class

**Find Out for Yourself**

1. Join the class in a brief discussion of today's activity. You might also take the time to think about the best ways to prepare slides of your specimens, and to ask your team for advice if you have any problem materials.

2. Now let the exploring begin. Go at your own pace. Share your discoveries with others on your team.

3. Use your notebook to record your observations. A quick sketch and a short set of descriptive words will help you remember the details of what you find.

4. After you clean up, share some of your most interesting observations with the class. Your teacher might invite you to draw what you saw on the chalkboard. Then you could leave your specimen in the learning center for the rest of the class to observe when they have free time.

5. Your teacher may ask you to help set up hay and grass infusions. Live organisms will grow in them. You will observe them in Lessons 15 and 16.

**Ideas to Explore**

1. What more can we do with the interesting objects you and your classmates brought in to observe? Here are a few ideas:

   ■ Measure the specimens in hair-widths or millimeters

   ■ Do some library research on the specimen and present your findings to the class

2. Read about and report to the class on scientists who have made important discoveries using the microscope: Louis Pasteur, Robert Koch, Alexander Fleming, and Edward Jenner.

3. If you didn't read it earlier, read the **Reading Selection** on Robert Hooke on pg. 35.

4. Write a creative story about a micronaut who journeys far into the mysterious interior of one of the specimens you examined today.

**Reading Selection**

### Taking a Look with Robert Hooke

Before he became a scientist Robert Hooke wanted to be a painter. He drew some very accurate, detailed drawings of the objects he observed under his microscope over 300 years ago.

Robert Hooke and Anton Leeuwenhoek lived at about the same time, in the middle of the 1600s. While Leeuwenhoek was busy building microscopes and looking at a great variety of microbes in his little shop in the Netherlands, Hooke was busy doing somewhat the same thing in England.

One of the differences between Leeuwenhoek and Hooke is that Hooke drew what he saw through his microscope. When he was young, Hooke thought he wanted to paint portraits. But then he went off to school, and college, and he became more interested in science. Hooke liked conducting experiments to find out more about the world around us.

While he was experimenting, Hooke learned a lot about what we call physics. And he invented some tools, such as the barometer, that help us determine what is happening in the physical world. (A barometer detects changes in pressure in the atmosphere, and these changes often indicate whether a storm is coming.) He also was interested in improving microscopes. His original microscope didn't have a lot of magnifying power. Hooke saw that the reason was because the lenses weren't curved enough, so he made his own microscope with a more rounded lens.

But with microscopes, Hooke really was more interested in what they could help him see. Using both simple (one lens) and compound (more than one lens) microscopes, he observed and carefully drew pictures of insects and their parts, the point of a needle, the edge of a razor, what he called insects in rainwater (they probably were microbes), snow crystals, and pieces of cork.

All of Hooke's drawings of what he saw under his microscopes are in a book entitled *Micrographia, or Some Physiological Descriptions of Minute Bodies Made by Magnifying Glasses with Observations and Inquiries Thereupon*. It was published in 1665. A copy of it can be found in the Special Collections Branch of the Smithsonian Institution Libraries. If you want to see a copy of this incredible picture book, you probably can! Just ask your librarian about helping you find the paperback edition.

**Figure 10-1**

*One of Hooke's microscopes (actual size about 9 inches tall)*

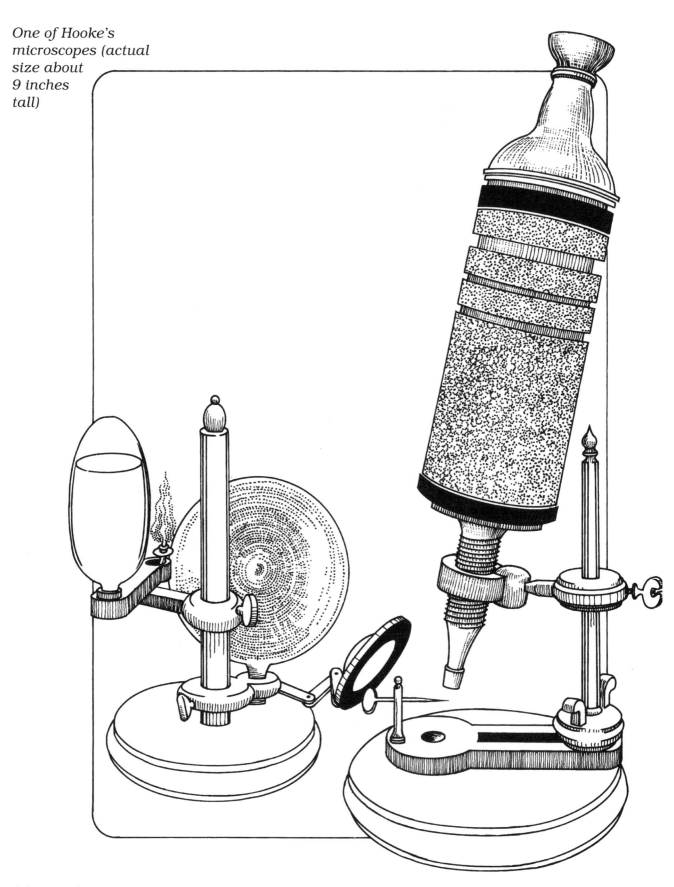

# Looking Inside an Onion

**Think and
Wonder**

When Robert Hooke looked at a sliver of cork under his microscope, he saw rows of "little empty boxes" that reminded him of rows of prison or monastery cells. He was the first to describe these structures, and in naming them coined a new use for the word "cell."

In this lesson you will move from the outside of an onion in, until you reach the smallest living unit, the cell.

**Materials**

*For you*

　1　**Activity Sheet 6, What's Inside an Onion?**
　1　microscope
　1　hand lens
　1　slide
　1　coverslip

*For each team*

　1　small onion
　1　water-dropper bottle
　1　pair of scissors
　1　pair of forceps
　4　toothpicks
　　　Paper towel or newspaper

**Find Out for
Yourself**

1. To warm up your observational skills, take a close look at the outside of your onion. Think of some good descriptive words to contribute to the class discussion on the exterior of the onion.

2. Next, preview **Activity Sheet 6** with the class. Note that you will make two different sketches at each level of observation. The first sketch records what you think, or predict, you will find as you look more and more closely at the onion. The second sketch records

what you actually see, or observe. Why should you not go back and correct your first drawings of what you predict you will see?

3. Now work on # 1, 2, 3, 4, and 5 on the **Activity Sheet**. While you are working, your teacher will move from group to group with the knife and cutting board.

    **Note:** If you blot the cut ends of the onion on paper towels, you may reduce some of the eye irritation.

4. For #6 on the **Activity Sheet** you will need to prepare a wet mount slide of the onion skin to look at under the microscope. You will need about half an onion ring. Here is what to do:

    ■ Separate the layers of the onion. Use your forceps or fingernails to carefully peel away a piece of the thin skin found between the layers.

    ■ Hold the onion skin with your forceps. Use scissors to snip off a piece about ½ inch long.

    ■ Lay this piece of onion skin flat on your slide. Be careful not to let it fold or wrinkle. Use the side of a toothpick to smooth it out.

    ■ Squeeze a drop or two of water on top of the onion skin and lower the coverslip or another slide on top.

*Figure 11-1*

*Removing onion skin with forceps*

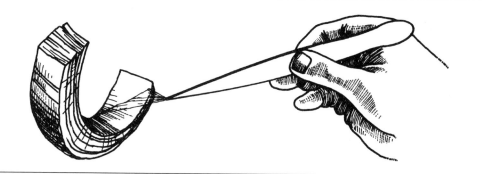

5. While you are looking at the onion under the microscope, experiment with the lighting conditions. Moving the mirror back and forth or using a hand to block the light will give you different views. You can create a bright field of view where the onion cell details appear dark, or you can create a dark field of view where the onion details appear white. Try both.

6. When you are finished, be sure to clean your slides well.

7. Join your class in a discussion of why cells are called "the building blocks of all living things."

8. Your teacher may assign you to do background reading on a fascinating organism, the *Volvox*.

**Ideas to Explore**

1. If a high-power microscope is available, take an even closer look at a cell.

2. What else can you find out about cells? Use your library to do some research.

3. There are lots of other plant cells that you can observe. Try:

   ■ Garlic. Use the same technique to prepare it as you did for the onion.

   ■ Lettuce. Slowly tear a leaf to expose a single layer of cells. Examine the torn edge for a flap of transparent skin. Make a wet-mount slide of it.

   ■ *Elodea*, an aquarium plant, has leaves with a double layer of cells. This is more challenging, but by making frequent focus adjustments, you may be able to get a good look at these cells.

*Figure 11-2*

Elodea

# Looking at Living Things: *Volvox*

By now you probably have become an expert at using your microscope, and feel ready for a new challenge: living creatures. Think about the reasons why you will need to be very skillful in order to observe living things.

Let's meet the first of your living specimens, ***Volvox.***

### *Volvox*

Commonly found in ponds, ***Volvox*** is a member of a large group of organisms known as green algae. Algae do not have roots, stems, or leaves, but, like green plants, they use light to make their own food by a process known as photosynthesis. Most algae live in the water, but you also may find them on damp surfaces, such as tree trunks, rocks, and soil.

***Volvox*** cells are especially interesting because they live together in colonies of 1,000 to 3,000 similar cells arranged in a hollow sphere. Each individual cell has two flagella, or whip like tails, that work together to propel the colony through the water. The spherical colony of cells is held together by a clear jelly like substance.

*Figure 12-1*

Volvox *colony*

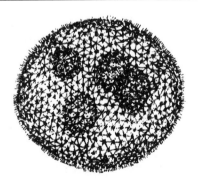

Also visible inside the sphere of many of the large colonies are smaller daughter colonies. After the daughter colonies become big enough, they will be released through an opening in the parent colony to become new, independent colonies.

There are advantages to colonial living. For example, because the *Volvox* colony is relatively large (350 to 600 micrometers), the tiny individual *Volvox* cells living in the colony are safe from the many microscopic animals that feed on other single-celled creatures.

*Volvox* is one of the beauties of the microscopic world. It is a rich bright green, and the whole globe rotates slowly through the water, reminding one of a delicate planet in graceful orbit.

## Materials

*For you*

1   student notebook

1   microscope

1   very clean well slide

1   piece of lens paper

1   coverslip

*For the class*

*Volvox* specimens and clean droppers

## Find Out for Yourself

1. Be sure to read the background information on *Volvox* on pg. 41.

2. Join your class in a brief discussion on the characteristics of *Volvox*. Think about these questions:

   - What do you expect to see under the microscope today? How will *Volvox* look? How many colonies might you see? Do you think you will be able to tell one colony from another? Do you think you will be able to see the individual cells that make up the colony?

   - How will looking at living things be different? What new challenges will you face?

3. Because these are living creatures, they need special handling. Watch and listen while your teacher explains how to pick up a specimen of *Volvox* from the distribution center as follows:

   - Using the clean dropper provided at the station, carefully draw up a very small amount of water from the bottom of the jar. Try not to agitate the jar or to stir up the water.

   - Place one drop of the water into a clean well slide, and put on the coverslip to prevent evaporation.

   - Gently return any water left in the dropper to the supply jar. Drop it in from close to the surface of the water, not from high up. It may contain many other live *Volvox*; you don't want to damage them.

4. Now begin your microbe hunt. Be persistent and don't give up. Keep scanning back and forth on the slide and focusing slowly up and down until you find *Volvox*. Then follow them around their pond. You might want to try different lighting effects, too.

5. In your notebook:

   ■ Make a drawing of a *Volvox* colony. Label the parts of the colony if possible.

   ■ Write a short description of what you observed. Include comments on colors and how the colony moves.

6. Clean up. Return specimens to the original container using the medicine dropper again. Rinse off the slide and coverslip in clean water.

7. Share your observations with the class.

**Ideas to Explore**

1. If you liked working with *Volvox*, you might want to investigate another flagellate. A flagellate is any microscopic creature having one or more flagella (a whip like tail), which it uses to move. A good example of another flagellate is the **Euglena**.

*Figure 12-2*

Euglena *under a microscope*

Euglena *and its flagella*

2. Did you know that algae are worth money? Do some research on algae as food. Algae can also cost people money. Find out about the killer algae that cause red tides.

3. Bring in other algae you find to look at under the microscope. Look for it in ponds, aquariums, or on the top of the soil of potted plants.

4. Have a brainstorm session with your classmates about other creatures that live in colonies. What are the advantages to these creatures of living together?

5. What would happen if you kept *Volvox* in the dark? Plan an experiment to find out.

# Looking at Living Things: *Blepharisma*

**Think and Wonder**

Let's continue pursuing moving microbes. Today, you will hunt down the rosy colored **Blepharisma**.

### Blepharisma

Commonly found in ponds, the **Blepharisma** is a single-celled, pear-shaped creature about 160 micrometers in length. It is unique because of its rosy coloration and easy to identify.

*Blepharisma's* size varies with its diet. Ordinarily, it mainly eats bacteria, but if its diet is enriched with other microbes, giant forms of *Blepharisma* may result. These hungry giants will then become cannibals and eat their own kind. You probably will not witness this drama, but you certainly will notice a great variation in size among the individuals on your slide.

This microbe belongs to a group called ciliates. A ciliate's body is covered with short, moveable, hair-like extensions called cilia. These cilia act like paddles to move the microbe through the water or to set up currents to force food into its mouth like opening.

*Figure 13-1*

Blepharisma *under the microscope*

Blepharisma *with its cilia*

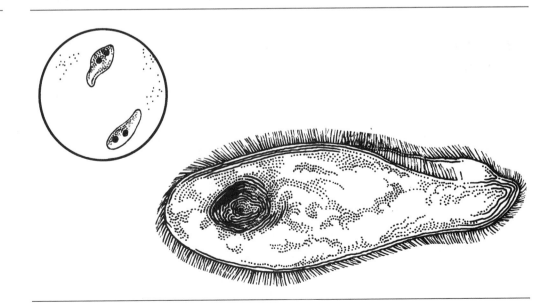

One way that the *Blepharisma* reproduces is by literally dividing itself in half. This process is called binary fission, and it produces two equal twins. There is a chance that someone in your class will see one of these cells in the process of binary fission.

*Figure 13-2*

Blepharisma *undergoing binary fission*

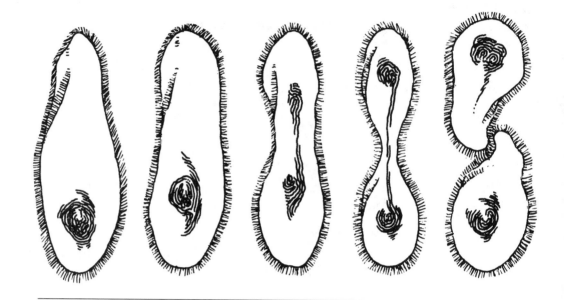

**Materials**

*For you*

1  student notebook
1  microscope
1  very clean well slide
1  piece of lens paper
1  coverslip

*For the class*

*Blepharisma* specimens and clean dropper

**Find Out for Yourself**

1. Did you read the background information on *Blepharisma* on pg. 45?

2. Now join your class in a brief discussion about *Blepharisma*. Think about these questions:

   ■ What do you expect to see under the microscope today? How will *Blepharisma* look? How will it move? How will it be different from *Volvox*?

   ■ What happens in binary fission?

3. Review how to mount a living microbe in a well slide:

- Using a clean dropper provided at the station, carefully draw up a very small amount of water. *Blepharisma* tend to cluster around the kernels of wheat at the bottom of the jar to feed on the bacteria found there, so aim the dropper in that direction. Try not to agitate the jar or stir up the water.

- Place one drop of water in the clean well slide, and put on the coverslip to prevent evaporation.

- Gently return any water left in the dropper to the supply jar. Drop it in from close to the surface of the water, not from high up. It may contain many other live *Blepharisma*; you don't want to harm them.

4. Now begin observing the rosy *Blepharisma*. Here are a few tips to help you in today's microbe hunt.

- Instead of trying to follow the *Blepharisma* around the slide, you might have more success keeping the slide in one place and concentrating on focusing up and down as individual microbes swim into view.

- Be on the lookout for any cells undergoing binary fission. If you do see a cell splitting, let your classmates take turns observing it, too. Your teacher may even want to set up your slide in the learning center for the class to observe at different times during the day.

- Try adjusting the light for different effects.

5. In your notebook:

- Make a drawing of at least one of the *Blepharisma* you observed. Label the parts if possible.

- Write a short description of what you observed. Include comments on colors, differences in sizes, and how the creature moves.

6. Clean up. Return specimens to the original container using the medicine dropper again. Rinse off the slide and coverslip in clean water.

7. Share your observations with the class.

**Ideas to Explore**

1. Did you find the *Blepharisma* interesting? If so, you may want to find out more about other ciliates. A ciliate is any microbe whose body is covered by short, hair like cilia. An interesting example is the ***Paramecium***.

*Figure 13-3*

Paramecium

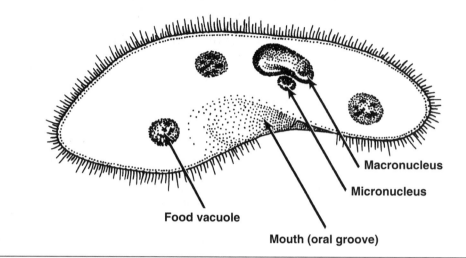

**Macronucleus**

**Micronucleus**

**Food vacuole**

**Mouth (oral groove)**

2. Write a story about an imaginary creature who splits itself in half to produce an identical twin. Why did it split? How long did it take? What were their names? Did they like each other?

# Looking at Living Things: Vinegar Eels

**Think and Wonder**

The *Volvox* and *Blepharisma* helped to prepare you to view the **vinegar eel** successfully. Both moved in unpredictable directions, and both swam in and out of focus. But neither one had the speed, size, or strength of the vinegar eel. Today, you will experiment with ways to slow down a very fast moving creature.

**Vinegar Eel**

The **vinegar eel** is not a fish at all but, rather, a harmless roundworm about 1.5 to 2 mm long, with points at both ends. Its smooth, slender body is nearly transparent, so it is possible to see its internal organs. Made up of many cells, this creature is large enough to be seen with the naked eye in bright light as it moves continuously in its vinegar environment. Few would call vinegar eels beautiful, but they certainly are fascinating.

*Figure 14-1*

*Vinegar eels under the microscope*

The vinegar eel has several distinctive features. It is one of the lowest animals to have a digestive tract complete with mouth and anus. Its method of reproduction is also distinctive. The embryos of the baby eels develop inside the female's body and are born alive and wiggling. The developing embryos are lined up inside the female's body by age, so you can see all stages of development through the mother's nearly transparent skin if you have a powerful microscope. Another interesting feature is that the eel actually spends its entire life in unpasteurized vinegar, a very acid environment indeed.

*Figure 14-2*

*Vinegar eel with embryos, enlarged*

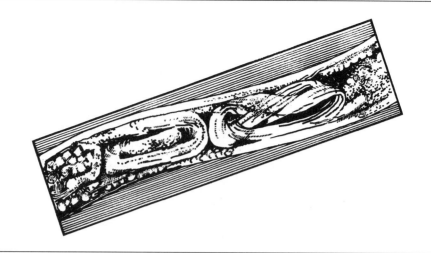

Why haven't you ever noticed vinegar eels shimmering at the edge of your vinegar bottle or swimming in your salad dressing? They simply aren't there, that's why. They live in unpasteurized cider vinegar, feeding on bacteria and tiny pieces of apple. But we use only pasteurized vinegar. **Pasteurization** is a process of heating the liquid to a high temperature to destroy microbes. It produces a sterilized vinegar, which completely eliminates the possibility of our finding these creatures on our kitchen shelf.

Even though the vinegar eels are quite large compared to *Volvox* and *Blepharisma*, they are a challenge to see through the microscope because of their tireless, rapid movement. They have muscles the whole length of their body and move through the vinegar with powerful whip like motions.

## Materials

*For you*

1   student notebook
1   microscope
1   very clean flat slide
1   piece of lens paper
1   coverslip (or a second flat slide as coverslip)

*For the class*

Vinegar eel culture and droppers

Cotton balls

Tissue paper or paper towels

Unflavored gelatin

Commercial slowing product (optional)

**Find Out for Yourself**

1. Be sure you have read and understood the background information on vinegar eels given on pg. 49.

2. Join in a brief discussion on vinegar eels. Think about these questions:

   ■ What do you expect to see when you look at vinegar eels under the microscope today? How will the eels move? How will they compare in size with *Volvox* and *Blepharisma*?

   ■ How do vinegar eels reproduce?

   ■ Why don't you see vinegar eels in ordinary kitchen vinegar?

3. Watch as your teacher demonstrates the best way to prepare a vinegar eel slide using a flat slide and a coverslip (or a second slide as a coverslip).

   ■ Using a clean dropper provided at the distribution station, draw up a very small amount of the vinegar. Vinegar eels will be visible around the edge of the jar at the surface, so hold the dropper in that area.

   ■ Place one drop of vinegar in the center of your clean slide, then lower the coverslip slowly into place. Try not to trap any air bubbles.

   ■ Gently return any vinegar left in the dropper to the supply jar. Drop it in from close to the surface of the vinegar, not from high up. It probably contains other live eels; you don't want to harm them.

4. Prepare your own slide carefully, then take time to observe what's on them. Here are a few tips:

   ■ As with the *Blepharisma*, you may have difficulty trying to follow the vinegar eels around the slide. Instead, you may do better to keep the slide in one place and concentrate on focusing up and down as individuals swim into view.

   ■ If you are having trouble finding vinegar eels on your slide, try looking at the edges of the coverslip.

   ■ Be sure to try different lighting effects. Since the vinegar eels are transparent, you may get much different views in bright light and dim light.

5. There are a number of ways to slow down the quick little vinegar eels. Once you have looked at them and appreciated how fast they really do move, you may be ready to experiment with some of these ways to slow them down. Use only one method at a time. Clean off your slide between preparations.

   ■ Touch a tissue paper or a paper towel to the edge of the coverslip and draw off some of the vinegar. By reducing the size of their pond, you restrict them to a smaller area.

- Then remove the coverslip and place several strands of cotton fiber pulled from a cotton ball on the drop of vinegar. Replace the coverslip. The vinegar eels will become trapped in the fibers.

- Try the same thing using strands of tissue paper or paper towel.

- Place a few grains of undissolved, unflavored gelatin in the vinegar on the slide. As the gelatin absorbs liquid and expands, it slows the vinegar eels considerably.

- Different commercial products are available from biological supply companies for slowing microscopic creatures. Be sure to follow the directions that come with the product you use.

6. In your notebook:

   - Make a drawing of one of the vinegar eels.

   - Add a few sentences to describe how the vinegar eel moves, its size, its color, and how you feel about observing it.

7. Clean up. Discard any specimens contaminated with fibers, gelatin, or commercial slowing products. Return any other specimens to the supply jar with the dropper. Rinse off the slides and coverslips in clean water.

## Final Activities

Join your class in reporting on your observations.

- Describe the vinegar eels. How do they look? How do they move? How do they compare in size to other creatures you have seen?

- Which methods did you try for slowing them down? What worked best for you?

- How did you feel observing the vinegar eels? Why was it an important activity?

## Ideas to Explore

1. Vinegar eels are not eels or fish. They are roundworms, and roundworms are one of the most plentiful of all animals on Earth. Roundworms can live in a wide variety of environments—soil, water, vinegar, or even inside human and animal bodies. Most are harmless, but there are a few really interesting "bad guys" you might want to learn more about. You might want to go to the library and look for information on some of the disease-causing roundworms, such as hookworms, pinworms, or trichina.

2. Here is an opportunity to plan and carry out an experiment. Vinegar is an acid liquid, yet vinegar eels spend their whole life right in it. Think of an experiment to find out how acid the environment needs to be for a vinegar eel to do well. Suppose you diluted the vinegar with water, for instance. How many drops of water would it take to

make a difference to the vinegar eel? How could you tell it was affecting the eel? What could you observe? What could you measure? How long would it take to notice any differences?

Make an experimental plan and discuss it with your teacher. Then, if your teacher approves, carry out the experiment.

# Looking at Living Things: Hay and Grass Infusions I

Several weeks ago the class helped prepare hay and grass infusions. Now it is time to see what has developed on a microscopic level.

Things have changed in the infusion jars. If all has gone well, the hay and grass have begun to decompose, the water has changed to an amber brown color, a film of scum floats on the surface, and there is a definite odor when you lift the lid.

What's happening? During the first few days after you set up the infusions, bacteria were responsible for most of the changes. Most bacteria are one-celled microbes, too small to see with our classroom microscopes. They were probably on the grass, on the jar, or on your hands when you set up the infusions. Some bacteria are harmful to humans and cause disease. Others are useful and are responsible for decomposition, the decay of organic material (such as the hay and grass in your infusions). Think of what a mess the world would be if nothing ever decomposed!

Soon after the bacteria began to grow and multiply, slightly larger, single-celled organisms appeared and began to feed on the bacteria. These larger organisms probably were also on the blades of grass or hay when you put them in the jar, but in a resting state. When conditions became favorable—when they reached water—they broke out of the protective coverings that had prevented them from drying out. Then these microbes began to feed on the bacteria and to grow and multiply, too. Since there are thousands of kinds of microscopic creatures, it is not possible to predict which ones landed in your particular infusions. So be prepared for just about anything to swim by!

**Materials**

*For you*

1   microscope
1   well slide
1   flat slide
2   coverslips
1   piece of lens paper
1   student notebook

*For the class*

Hay and grass infusions and droppers
Cotton balls
Unflavored gelatin
Tissue paper or paper towels

**Ideas to Explore**

1.  Be sure to read the background information on hay and grass infusions on pg. 55.

2.  Join in a brief discussion on hay and grass infusions. Think about these questions:

    ■   No one in class knows yet what kinds of microbes we will find in the hay and grass infusions. But we are fairly certain microbes are there. What changes have you noticed in the jars that might be evidence that microbes are present in the infusions?

    ■   This may be your most challenging microbe hunt yet. The microbes may be very small and fast moving. There might be very few of them on some of your slides. But don't give up. If you don't find something on the first slide, try and try again. What special techniques have you learned that might be helpful in viewing your microbes today?

    ■   When you do find some microbes, how will you tell one from the other?

3.  Now get busy on your tasks for today. Here they are:

    ■   Prepare at least two good slides. Make them from two different infusions. Use good judgment, and work carefully. Try any of the special techniques you have learned.

    ■   Find and observe at least one microbe, more if possible.

    ■   In your notebook, make a quick sketch of at least one microbe, more if possible. Label the sketches with the date and tell which infusions they came from.

    ■   Write a few brief sentences describing the microbes. Include information on their size, shape, color, and motion.

■ Give your microbes creative but descriptive names to help you remember them. For example, *Blepharisma* might be called "Pinky Pear shape."

4. Today is a first look at the infusions. Try to see as much as you can and record it very quickly for future reference. You will come back to the infusions in the next lesson for a much closer look.

   While you are working on the activity, your teacher will probably be observing you and making notes on your progress.

5. Clean up. Return uncontaminated specimens to the infusion jars they came from. Rinse your slides thoroughly and lay them out to air dry.

## Final Activities

Congratulations! You have made great progress. Now share some of your discoveries with your classmates. You may want to show your drawings or sketch them on the chalkboard. Give a verbal presentation, too, and share the name you gave to your creatures. It will be interesting to see if other classmates made any of the same discoveries you did.

## Ideas to Explore

In ancient times, some people believed that mice sprang to life out of piles of old rags and that horse hairs that fell into water became worms. Others believed that it was impossible for living things to come to life from dead or rotting materials and that they could only come from other living things. The arguments on each side raged for years.

But, in 1858, a French chemist named Louis Pasteur set out to prove that living things are produced only by other living things like themselves. In a famous set of experiments, he did just that. What can you find out about these famous experiments? Share your information with the class.

# Looking at Living Things: Hay and Grass Infusions II

**Think and Wonder**

In Lesson 15, you scanned several slides, took a quick look at as many microbes as you could, made some fast sketches to help you remember what you saw, and jotted a few descriptive sentences. Today, the pace slows down. Now you can concentrate all of your efforts on just one microbe.

What do you think you might see today? It is possible that you may see some of the same microbes as last time. It is also possible that these microbes have grown, died, been eaten by bigger microbes, or changed in some other way so that you don't recognize them. This is another challenging situation, but you should be ready for it.

**Materials**

*For you*

    1  microscope
    1  well slide
    1  flat slide
    2  coverslips
    1  piece of lens paper
    1  student notebook

*For the class*

    Hay and grass infusions and droppers
    Cotton balls
    Unflavored gelatin
    Tissue paper or paper towels

**Find Out for Yourself**

1.  Let's review what you did in the last lesson:

    ■  What kinds of slides did you prepare? Which worked well for you?

■ What kinds of creatures did you see? Do you think you will see the same ones again today?

2. Lesson 15 was a good warm-up for today's activities. You will do some of the very same things, but with more care and precision. Here are your tasks:

■ Prepare one really good slide. It should be clear, without bubbles, and have visible microbes on it. It may take more than one try to prepare one really good slide. Keep working at it until you have made the best slide you can.

■ Find and observe one microbe in detail. If necessary, use any of the techniques you have learned to slow it down.

■ Make a drawing or several drawings of different views of the microbe you observed. Label the drawing(s) with the date and tell which infusion the microbe came from. Try to make your drawing(s) clear, accurate, and complete.

■ Write a paragraph or more to describe your microbe. Include information on:

– Size (a good way to talk about size is to compare this microbe to something else, like another microbe, a hair-width, or spaces in the screen wire)

– Shape, especially if it changes

– Color

– Motion

– Speed

■ Give the microbe a creative but descriptive name.

While you are working on the activity, your teacher will be observing you and making notes on your progress.

3. When you are finished, do your share to help clean up all of the equipment and return it to the containers it came in.

4. Share your work with the class—your drawings and your writings.

**Ideas to Explore**

If you are not ready to leave the subject of microbes yet, you may have some ideas for other projects you would like to do. Discuss those ideas with your class.

Here are a few to get you started:

■ A Microbial Lunch featuring food items made from microscopic creatures (like algae) or produced by microbes (like yogurt).

■ A Microworlds Mural featuring some of your favorite microbes.

■ Three-dimensional models of microbes

- An interview with a famous microbe, like the one that caused the bubonic plague, *Yersinia pestis*.

- Presentations of your research involving microbes. Maybe you could show your drawings, too. What would be a good way to do that?

*Figure 16-1*

*Microbial Lunch*

*Figure 16-2*

*Microworlds Mural*

# Glossary

**Algae:** A group of simple plants that live in water or damp areas. Algae have no roots, stems, or leaves.

**Amphibian:** An organism that breathes through gills when it is young and through lungs when it becomes an adult. Frogs and salamanders are amphibians.

**Analyze:** To study something by breaking it down into simpler parts.

**Bacteria:** Single-celled microorganisms. Some bacteria cause diseases, but most of them are harmless, or even beneficial, to humans.

**Barometer:** An instrument used to detect changes in the pressure in the atmosphere.

**Binary fission:** The process by which a cell divides into two parts.

**Blepharisma:** A single-celled, pear-shaped microorganism that is often found in pond water.

**Cannibal:** An animal that eats its own kind.

**Cilia:** Short, hairlike extensions that act like paddles to help a microorganism move through the water.

**Classify:** To group things together because they share one or more properties.

**Colony:** A population of one species of organism living in a particular place.

**Conclusion:** A decision that is based on observation or on a study of data.

**Constant:** A condition that is not changed in a scientific experiment.

**Contaminate:** To soil, stain, or infect by contact; to make impure.

**Controlled experiment:** A scientific investigation in which one variable is changed and all the others are kept the same, or constant.

**Convex:** Curved or rounded on the outside, like a bowl.

**Coverslip:** A piece of glass or clear plastic that is placed over the specimen on a microscope slide.

**Data:** Information, such as that gathered during an experiment.

**Decay:** The process by which dead organic material breaks down.

**Decomposition:** The process by which organic materials break up and decay.

**Diameter:** The length of a straight line that passes directly through the center of a circle or sphere, from one side to the other.

**Euglena:** A member of a group of one-celled microorganisms. A distinguishing feature of euglena is a long, whiplike structure, called a flagellum, that helps it move through the water.

**Evidence:** Something that offers proof.

**Experiment:** A procedure that is carried out to investigate a scientific question.

**Field of view:** The maximum area that is visible through the lens of a microscope.

**Flagellum (plural, flagella):** Long, whiplike structures that help some microorganisms move about in water.

**Focus:** To adjust the position of a lens in order to make a clear image.

**Hypothesis:** A prediction about how something works or how two variables are related.

**Inference:** A conclusion based on evidence.

**Infusion:** A watery mixture of decaying organic matter.

**Internal:** Being, or taking place, inside someone or some thing.

**Invent:** To think up or create something for the first time.

**Lens:** A piece of curved glass or other clear material that bends light rays. Lenses can help make things look clearer, larger, or closer.

**Magnifier:** A tool that makes something appear larger than it is.

**Microbe:** A tiny organism that can be seen only under magnification; a microorganism.

**Micrometer:** A unit used to measure very tiny objects.

**Microscope:** A device for viewing things that are too small be seen with the eye alone.

**Microscopic:** Too small to be seen without a microscope.

**Opinion:** An expression of how one thinks or feels about something. An opinion is based on personal views, not necessarily on facts.

**Organism:** A living creature.

**Paramecium (plural, paramecia):** A one-celled, slipper-shaped microorganism that lives in fresh water.

**Pasteurize:** To heat a liquid at a high enough temperature and for a long enough time to kill harmful bacteria and then to cool the liquid quickly.

**Pattern:** A repeating arrangement of shapes, colors, numbers, or other things.

**Reflect:** To give back an image or likeness. Also, to think seriously about something.

**Reproduce:** To produce new organisms of the same species.

**Slide:** A small piece of glass or plastic used to hold specimens to be examined under a microscope.

**Specimen:** A sample that is used to represent an entire group.

**Sterilize:** To make free of living microorganisms.

**Transparent:** Clear; able to let light through undistorted.

**Variable:** An element in an experiment that can be changed.

**Vinegar eel:** A roundworm that lives in vinegar. It has a transparent body and can be seen without a microscope.

**Volvox:** A member of a group of microorganisms known as the green algae. Volvox live in colonies of 1,000–3,000 cells, arranged in a hollow sphere.

**Weathering:** The process by which earth materials are broken down by natural forces.

**Weight:** A measurement of the force of gravity on an object.

**Well slide:** A microscope slide with shallow dent. Used to hold thick specimens, either wet or dry.

**Wet-mount slide:** Two microscope slides, or a slide and coverslip, with a drop of liquid between them.